I Fill My Cup

A Journal for Compassionate Helpers

Lisa Hutchison LMHC

Divine Channel Publishing

Copyright Page

ISBN: 978-0-578-43995-2

Printed in the United States of America by Divine Channel Publishing

First Printing, 2019

http://www.lisahutchison.net

Dedication Page

This journal is dedicated to all of the sensitive, compassionate helpers who have enriched my life throughout the years. You make the world a better place to be in, thank you.

To God, the Divine Source of all that is, thank you for the inspiration, courage and guidance to bring this journal and all of my writings into physical form.

To my husband and best friend, Jamie, thank you for your encouragement, love and belief in my creative work.

To my friend, Carol, thank you for your unconditional love, support and feedback for this journal, my work and life.

To Debra Oakland, Author of *Change Your Movie, Change Your Life: 7 Reel Concepts for Courageous Change*, thank you for your suggestions, feedback and encouragement.

To Tae Lynne, Author of *Color the World with Kindness*, thank you for your advice, recommendations and support.

To my family and friends, who are now deceased and those who are living. Thank you for your acknowledgement and support of my writing. I appreciate all of your purchases, reviews, social media likes, tweets and comments.

A Note from the Author

As a licensed mental health counselor and empath, I understand the energy drain compassionate helpers experience. Your focus is on other people's needs. At the end of the day, whether you work from home or arrive back there, you are exhausted. All you want to do is tune out with the TV, social media or a glass of wine. When you engage in these types of distraction activities, while you are already depleted, it can lead to illness and burnt-out.

I created this journal to help you identify exactly where you are disconnected and help you restore your vital energy. I believe and trust, you have the answers within you. With these prompts, you will build awareness around any energy depletion issues and become empowered to choose different behaviors and thoughts. You cannot add more hours into your day, but you can feel more energized and get more done.

If you need more assistance or support in this journey of energetic discovery, please feel free to contact me for a counseling or coaching session. Both of these services are offered in person and by phone.

Be as good to yourself as you are to others.

Many Blessings,

Lisa

Lisa Hutchison LMHC at http://www.lisahutchison.net

How to Use This Journal

I recommend writing in this journal, daily, in order to understand your unique energy patterns. The questions can be answered when you return home from work or right before you go to bed. If you forget or cannot seem to write daily, a couple of times a week is okay. The idea is to raise your energy awareness in order to make some life changes.

1.) Know your type: Are you Introvert, Extrovert or Ambivert?

You do not need to take a formal test to know. Each day you are asked this question because you may feel a different energy within when you interact with the world. Personality can be fluid rather than static, meaning one day you feel extroverted, another introverted or one morning feels introverted and the afternoon more extroverted. This is not meant to confuse you. I want to help you define your own energy in a way that makes sense for you. Read the descriptions, connect with your intuition, and record your energy type.

Introverts feel most energized when they spend time alone or do solitary activities, such as walking in nature, reading a book or silently gazing out a window.

Extroverts feel most energized when they are connecting with other people, having conversations or debates.

Ambiverts are a combination of introvert and extrovert energy. You may enjoy interacting with others, yet need your alone time to recharge. Some say ambiverts are really just introverts. I like this category because many of my clients do not feel comfortable in one category.

2.) Rate your energy using the energy scale on the next page. At each level, you will find suggestions to replenish your energy.

3.) Identify and write down your specific energy depletion issues using the prompts on each journal entry page.

4.) Increase your awareness and develop a plan to either protect or refill your energy. A few suggestions have been given to you within the energy scale and plan to protect your energy pages.

5.) Commit to your goals and complete them. An intention for this journal: *I complete these exercises not only for myself but also for those I serve.* Feel free to write your own personalized intention in your daily journal entry.

The Energy Scale

1 *"Warning Low Fuel"*- At this level, you experience energy depletion and numbness. This type of disconnection happens to everyone, as it is a part of the life experience, although it is meant to be temporary. It is often seen when you go through a major life crisis such as a loss, death or an event that pulls the rug out from under you. Action needs to be taken to prevent illness or a decrease in physical, mental or spiritual health.

This can also be the result of doing too much for too long, as in the case of burnout. When you exist in survival mode, you detach emotionally, physically and spiritually. It is as if you are running on autopilot, getting what needs to be done, done.

Begin with yoga, meditation, grounding and connecting to the earth. Check if one or more of your chakras are out of balance. If you are struggling, it is recommended you receive grounding assistance through an energy professional (reiki or shamanism) to reconnect to your inner most self.

2 *"Too Many Feelings"*- Connection is re-established in mind, body and spirit. You experience feelings of overwhelm, anxiety, guilt and creative blocks from too many emotions. As the energy starts to flow, these dormant feelings re-awaken. It is important to find someone comfortable, safe and stable, to share these moods with. At this level, you need to process these unconscious feelings creatively or with a licensed psychotherapist.

3 *"Stickin' Thinking"*- You experience fear and creative blocks from judgmental, self-critical thoughts because your energy is stuck in distorted beliefs. Assistance from individual therapy or a group therapy/self-help group can help you reframe and restructure these thoughts.

4 *"Lacking Confidence"*- Energy returns as you start to feel and think more clearly, yet you lack confidence and motivation. Unsure of your life purpose, you feel inferior and are triggered to react. Feeling vulnerable, you avoid the spotlight and overcompensate/over help to put your focus on others. It is difficult to commit to one course of action because your thoughts and energy are scattered. Assertiveness training is recommended by a licensed professional.

5 *"Getting By"*- You have your moments and are using coping skills. Life is not perfect, but you are doing it! There are some motivational issues, but you are able

to push through the day. Consider lifestyle changes, stress management techniques, assertiveness, and life skills counseling.

6 *"The Wounded Helper"*- You feel good at times and are able to heal yourself and others, yet your giving and receiving are out of balance. You experience occasional bouts of depletion but are able to bounce back using self-care skills and therapy sessions for support. Mindfulness and assertiveness training are helpful at this stage to maintain your awareness and energy.

7 *"Feeling Tongue Tied"*- Your personal expression is blocked with words and writing, causing you to feel uncomfortable to speak your truth. It is as if you have a lot to say, yet cannot seem to get it out to others or yourself. Some helpful modalities are expressive arts therapy, chanting, singing and writing coaching.

8 *"Feeling Happy and Hopeful"*- Your communication is effective with speaking and/or writing. You experience difficulty trusting the intuition you receive through premonitions, messages and dreams. Practice listening within during meditation; your soul's guidance will lead the way. Intuitive counseling can be helpful with this stage.

9 *"I Feel GOOD"*- You may question your life's purpose at times, overall you trust and know there is a plan for your life. You experience occasional sleep issues with the overflow of intuitive and creative inspirations. Relaxation and lifestyle counseling may benefit you.

10 *"Ready to Rock and Roll"*- Everything is great. You feel and look good. You are open to creativity, receive synchronicities and are in the flow of life. Enjoy!

Plan to Protect Your Energy

As a compassionate helper, it is important to learn how to protect your energies from toxic people, places and situations. Here are a few helpful tips to get you started.

Assertiveness & Boundaries

Assertiveness helps you to speak up and ask for what you want in a clear and effective manner. Boundaries are invisible limits that protect your energy. Assertiveness and boundaries often go hand and hand. When you voice your preferences, you have a higher likelihood of getting what you want. Some examples of assertive boundary statements are:

I feel_____ when you _____.

I like this_____.

Honor your heart and practice saying no when you do not want to do something. Sometimes saying no means saying yes to your own life.

Holding the space

Holding the space is a healthy way of interacting with others who are hurting, without getting depleted energy wise. It is a type of boundary for sensitive healers which benefits both parties because you are not getting entangled or engulfed in the other person's emotions. This practice contains your energy while you help others and allows the other person to feel seen, honored and acknowledged.

How does it work?

Holding the space is about practicing mindfulness within and around your body. When you are present in your body, you become a witness to what is happening without getting attached to a feeling, thought or sensation. Sounds simple, right? Do not get discouraged because it takes practice to be in this frame of mind and slow your energy down. When you can offer this to others, it is a healing gift for them and an energy booster for yourself.

Remember these 3 words; listen, allow and be present.

When you practice empathic listening during emotional times of releasing, it lets people know you are with them and they can share their pain with you. This is empathy in action! If you feel compelled to speak, validate what the other person says by rephrasing what they said and ask them to tell you more about an important part of the story.

Claim your space

As a sensitive person, are you taking up enough space? When a compassionate helper gets drained, he or she closes off the physical space around him or her. You see this in people who often sit with their arms crossed or body hunched over. This is done as a subconscious attempt to protect your energy from becoming invaded by other people's thoughts and feelings. The problem with this type of defense is you end up closed off from receiving love and positive energy. Practice sitting and standing with a more open stance, while breathing deeply.

It has to be about you!

Whenever I say it is all about you, compassionate helpers cringe. The last thing you want is to be considered selfish or self-absorbed. (Like that could ever happen!) Focusing on you is about being healthy. This means getting your own healing and therapy in order to take care of yourself and your energy. Healings release toxins and replenish energy, while therapy takes you a step further to uncover subconscious patterns, which breaks the energy depletion cycle. The combination of both modalities will keep you balanced and well. When you work on yourself, you help others by modeling what is healthy behavior.

Journal Entries

Date: _____

Right Now I Feel: ___ Introvert __ Extrovert __ Ambivert

Rate Your Energy Level: _____

Prompts:

[ ] Where did I lose energy today in my body, mind and spirit?

[ ] Who or what do I need to be aware of and why?

[ ] When did I feel good today? When did I not?

[ ] How can I replenish and recharge my energy?

[ ] What is one positive step I will take to protect my energy?

[ ] What are 5 positives about me?

_____

_____

_____

_____

_____

_____

_____

_____

_____

_____

_____

_____

_____

_____

_____

_____

_____

_____

_____

_____

_____

_____

_____

Journal Entries

Date: _____

Right Now I Feel: ___ Introvert __ Extrovert __ Ambivert

Rate Your Energy Level: _____

Prompts:

[ ] Where did I lose energy today in my body, mind and spirit?

[ ] Who or what do I need to be aware of and why?

[ ] When did I feel good today? When did I not?

[ ] How can I replenish and recharge my energy?

[ ] What is one positive step I will take to protect my energy?

[ ] What are 5 positives about me?

_____

_____

_____

_____

_____

_____

_____

_____

_____

_____

_____

_____

_____

_____

_____

_____

_____

_____

_____

_____

_____

_____

Journal Entries

Date: _____

Right Now I Feel: ___ Introvert __ Extrovert __ Ambivert

Rate Your Energy Level: _____

Prompts:

[ ] Where did I lose energy today in my body, mind and spirit?

[ ] Who or what do I need to be aware of and why?

[ ] When did I feel good today? When did I not?

[ ] How can I replenish and recharge my energy?

[ ] What is one positive step I will take to protect my energy?

[ ] What are 5 positives about me?

_____

_____

_____

_____

_____

_____

_____

_____

_____

_____

_____

_____

_____

_____

_____

_____

_____

_____

_____

_____

_____

Journal Entries

Date: _____

Right Now I Feel: ___ Introvert __ Extrovert __ Ambivert

Rate Your Energy Level: _____

Prompts:

[ ] Where did I lose energy today in my body, mind and spirit?

[ ] Who or what do I need to be aware of and why?

[ ] When did I feel good today? When did I not?

[ ] How can I replenish and recharge my energy?

[ ] What is one positive step I will take to protect my energy?

[ ] What are 5 positives about me?

_____

_____

_____

_____

_____

_____

_____

_____

_____

_____

_____

_____

_____

_____

_____

_____

_____

_____

_____

_____

_____

Journal Entries

Date: _____

Right Now I Feel: ___ Introvert __ Extrovert __ Ambivert

Rate Your Energy Level: _____

Prompts:

[ ] Where did I lose energy today in my body, mind and spirit?

[ ] Who or what do I need to be aware of and why?

[ ] When did I feel good today? When did I not?

[ ] How can I replenish and recharge my energy?

[ ] What is one positive step I will take to protect my energy?

[ ] What are 5 positives about me?

_____
_____
_____
_____
_____
_____
_____
_____
_____
_____
_____
_____
_____
_____
_____
_____
_____
_____
_____
_____
_____
_____
_____
_____

Journal Entries

Date: _____

Right Now I Feel: ___ Introvert __ Extrovert __ Ambivert

Rate Your Energy Level: _____

Prompts:

[ ] Where did I lose energy today in my body, mind and spirit?

[ ] Who or what do I need to be aware of and why?

[ ] When did I feel good today? When did I not?

[ ] How can I replenish and recharge my energy?

[ ] What is one positive step I will take to protect my energy?

[ ] What are 5 positives about me?

_____

_____

_____

_____

_____

_____

_____

_____

_____

_____

_____

_____

_____

_____

_____

_____

_____

_____

_____

_____

_____

_____

_____

Journal Entries

Date: _____

Right Now I Feel: ___ Introvert __ Extrovert __ Ambivert

Rate Your Energy Level: _____

Prompts:

[ ] Where did I lose energy today in my body, mind and spirit?

[ ] Who or what do I need to be aware of and why?

[ ] When did I feel good today? When did I not?

[ ] How can I replenish and recharge my energy?

[ ] What is one positive step I will take to protect my energy?

[ ] What are 5 positives about me?

_____

_____

_____

_____

_____

_____

_____

_____

_____

_____

_____

_____

_____

_____

_____

_____

_____

_____

_____

_____

_____

_____

_____

Journal Entries

Date: _____

Right Now I Feel: ___ Introvert __ Extrovert __ Ambivert

Rate Your Energy Level: _____

Prompts:

[ ] Where did I lose energy today in my body, mind and spirit?

[ ] Who or what do I need to be aware of and why?

[ ] When did I feel good today? When did I not?

[ ] How can I replenish and recharge my energy?

[ ] What is one positive step I will take to protect my energy?

[ ] What are 5 positives about me?

_____

_____

_____

_____

_____

_____

_____

_____

_____

_____

_____

_____

_____

_____

_____

_____

_____

_____

_____

_____

_____

_____

Journal Entries

Date: _____

Right Now I Feel: ___ Introvert __ Extrovert __ Ambivert

Rate Your Energy Level: _____

Prompts:

[ ] Where did I lose energy today in my body, mind and spirit?

[ ] Who or what do I need to be aware of and why?

[ ] When did I feel good today? When did I not?

[ ] How can I replenish and recharge my energy?

[ ] What is one positive step I will take to protect my energy?

[ ] What are 5 positives about me?

_____
_____
_____
_____
_____
_____
_____
_____
_____
_____
_____
_____
_____
_____
_____
_____
_____
_____
_____
_____
_____
_____

Journal Entries

Date: _____

Right Now I Feel: ___ Introvert __ Extrovert __ Ambivert

Rate Your Energy Level: _____

Prompts:

[ ] Where did I lose energy today in my body, mind and spirit?

[ ] Who or what do I need to be aware of and why?

[ ] When did I feel good today? When did I not?

[ ] How can I replenish and recharge my energy?

[ ] What is one positive step I will take to protect my energy?

[ ] What are 5 positives about me?

_____

_____

_____

_____

_____

_____

_____

_____

_____

_____

_____

_____

_____

_____

_____

_____

_____

_____

_____

_____

_____

_____

Journal Entries

Date: _____

Right Now I Feel: ___ Introvert __ Extrovert __ Ambivert

Rate Your Energy Level: _____

Prompts:

[ ] Where did I lose energy today in my body, mind and spirit?

[ ] Who or what do I need to be aware of and why?

[ ] When did I feel good today? When did I not?

[ ] How can I replenish and recharge my energy?

[ ] What is one positive step I will take to protect my energy?

[ ] What are 5 positives about me?

_____

_____

_____

_____

_____

_____

_____

_____

_____

_____

_____

_____

_____

_____

_____

_____

_____

_____

_____

_____

_____

Journal Entries

Date: _____

Right Now I Feel: ___ Introvert ___ Extrovert ___ Ambivert

Rate Your Energy Level: _____

Prompts:

[ ] Where did I lose energy today in my body, mind and spirit?

[ ] Who or what do I need to be aware of and why?

[ ] When did I feel good today? When did I not?

[ ] How can I replenish and recharge my energy?

[ ] What is one positive step I will take to protect my energy?

[ ] What are 5 positives about me?

_____

_____

_____

_____

_____

_____

_____

_____

_____

_____

_____

_____

_____

_____

_____

_____

_____

_____

_____

_____

_____

_____

_____

_____

Journal Entries

Date: _____

Right Now I Feel: ___ Introvert ___ Extrovert ___ Ambivert

Rate Your Energy Level: _____

Prompts:

[ ] Where did I lose energy today in my body, mind and spirit?

[ ] Who or what do I need to be aware of and why?

[ ] When did I feel good today? When did I not?

[ ] How can I replenish and recharge my energy?

[ ] What is one positive step I will take to protect my energy?

[ ] What are 5 positives about me?

_____

_____

_____

_____

_____

_____

_____

_____

_____

_____

_____

_____

_____

_____

_____

_____

_____

_____

_____

_____

_____

_____

_____

Journal Entries

Date: _____

Right Now I Feel: ___ Introvert __ Extrovert __ Ambivert

Rate Your Energy Level: _____

Prompts:

[ ] Where did I lose energy today in my body, mind and spirit?

[ ] Who or what do I need to be aware of and why?

[ ] When did I feel good today? When did I not?

[ ] How can I replenish and recharge my energy?

[ ] What is one positive step I will take to protect my energy?

[ ] What are 5 positives about me?

_____

_____

_____

_____

_____

_____

_____

_____

_____

_____

_____

_____

_____

_____

_____

_____

_____

_____

_____

_____

_____

_____

_____

Journal Entries

Date: _____

Right Now I Feel: ___ Introvert ___ Extrovert ___ Ambivert

Rate Your Energy Level: _____

Prompts:

[ ] Where did I lose energy today in my body, mind and spirit?

[ ] Who or what do I need to be aware of and why?

[ ] When did I feel good today? When did I not?

[ ] How can I replenish and recharge my energy?

[ ] What is one positive step I will take to protect my energy?

[ ] What are 5 positives about me?

_____

_____

_____

_____

_____

_____

_____

_____

_____

_____

_____

_____

_____

_____

_____

_____

_____

_____

_____

_____

_____

_____

_____

Journal Entries

Date: _____

Right Now I Feel: ___ Introvert __ Extrovert __ Ambivert

Rate Your Energy Level: _____

Prompts:

[ ] Where did I lose energy today in my body, mind and spirit?

[ ] Who or what do I need to be aware of and why?

[ ] When did I feel good today? When did I not?

[ ] How can I replenish and recharge my energy?

[ ] What is one positive step I will take to protect my energy?

[ ] What are 5 positives about me?

_____

_____

_____

_____

_____

_____

_____

_____

_____

_____

_____

_____

_____

_____

_____

_____

_____

_____

_____

_____

_____

_____

_____

Journal Entries

Date: _____

Right Now I Feel: ___ Introvert __ Extrovert __ Ambivert

Rate Your Energy Level: _____

Prompts:

[ ] Where did I lose energy today in my body, mind and spirit?

[ ] Who or what do I need to be aware of and why?

[ ] When did I feel good today? When did I not?

[ ] How can I replenish and recharge my energy?

[ ] What is one positive step I will take to protect my energy?

[ ] What are 5 positives about me?

_____
_____
_____
_____
_____
_____
_____
_____
_____
_____
_____
_____
_____
_____
_____
_____
_____
_____
_____
_____
_____
_____
_____

Journal Entries

Date: _____

Right Now I Feel: ___ Introvert __ Extrovert __ Ambivert

Rate Your Energy Level: _____

Prompts:

[ ] Where did I lose energy today in my body, mind and spirit?

[ ] Who or what do I need to be aware of and why?

[ ] When did I feel good today? When did I not?

[ ] How can I replenish and recharge my energy?

[ ] What is one positive step I will take to protect my energy?

[ ] What are 5 positives about me?

_____

_____

_____

_____

_____

_____

_____

_____

_____

_____

_____

_____

_____

_____

_____

_____

_____

_____

_____

_____

Journal Entries

Date: _____

Right Now I Feel: ___ Introvert __ Extrovert __ Ambivert

Rate Your Energy Level: _____

Prompts:

[ ] Where did I lose energy today in my body, mind and spirit?

[ ] Who or what do I need to be aware of and why?

[ ] When did I feel good today? When did I not?

[ ] How can I replenish and recharge my energy?

[ ] What is one positive step I will take to protect my energy?

[ ] What are 5 positives about me?

_____

_____

_____

_____

_____

_____

_____

_____

_____

_____

_____

_____

_____

_____

_____

_____

_____

_____

_____

_____

_____

_____

Journal Entries

Date: _____

Right Now I Feel: ___ Introvert ___ Extrovert ___ Ambivert

Rate Your Energy Level: _____

Prompts:

[ ] Where did I lose energy today in my body, mind and spirit?

[ ] Who or what do I need to be aware of and why?

[ ] When did I feel good today? When did I not?

[ ] How can I replenish and recharge my energy?

[ ] What is one positive step I will take to protect my energy?

[ ] What are 5 positives about me?

_____

_____

_____

_____

_____

_____

_____

_____

_____

_____

_____

_____

_____

_____

_____

_____

_____

_____

_____

_____

_____

_____

Journal Entries

Date: _____

Right Now I Feel: ___ Introvert __ Extrovert __ Ambivert

Rate Your Energy Level: _____

Prompts:

[ ] Where did I lose energy today in my body, mind and spirit?

[ ] Who or what do I need to be aware of and why?

[ ] When did I feel good today? When did I not?

[ ] How can I replenish and recharge my energy?

[ ] What is one positive step I will take to protect my energy?

[ ] What are 5 positives about me?

_____

_____

_____

_____

_____

_____

_____

_____

_____

_____

_____

_____

_____

_____

_____

_____

_____

_____

_____

_____

_____

_____

Journal Entries

Date: _____

Right Now I Feel: ___ Introvert __ Extrovert __ Ambivert

Rate Your Energy Level: _____

Prompts:

[ ] Where did I lose energy today in my body, mind and spirit?

[ ] Who or what do I need to be aware of and why?

[ ] When did I feel good today? When did I not?

[ ] How can I replenish and recharge my energy?

[ ] What is one positive step I will take to protect my energy?

[ ] What are 5 positives about me?

_____

_____

_____

_____

_____

_____

_____

_____

_____

_____

_____

_____

_____

_____

_____

_____

_____

_____

_____

_____

_____

_____

Journal Entries

Date: _____

Right Now I Feel: ___ Introvert __ Extrovert __ Ambivert

Rate Your Energy Level: _____

Prompts:

[ ] Where did I lose energy today in my body, mind and spirit?

[ ] Who or what do I need to be aware of and why?

[ ] When did I feel good today? When did I not?

[ ] How can I replenish and recharge my energy?

[ ] What is one positive step I will take to protect my energy?

[ ] What are 5 positives about me?

_____
_____
_____
_____
_____
_____
_____
_____
_____
_____
_____
_____
_____
_____
_____
_____
_____
_____
_____
_____
_____
_____
_____
_____

Journal Entries

Date: _____

Right Now I Feel: ___ Introvert __ Extrovert __ Ambivert

Rate Your Energy Level: _____

Prompts:

[ ] Where did I lose energy today in my body, mind and spirit?

[ ] Who or what do I need to be aware of and why?

[ ] When did I feel good today? When did I not?

[ ] How can I replenish and recharge my energy?

[ ] What is one positive step I will take to protect my energy?

[ ] What are 5 positives about me?

_____

_____

_____

_____

_____

_____

_____

_____

_____

_____

_____

_____

_____

_____

_____

_____

_____

_____

_____

_____

_____

Journal Entries

Date: _____

Right Now I Feel: ___ Introvert __ Extrovert __ Ambivert

Rate Your Energy Level: _____

Prompts:

[ ] Where did I lose energy today in my body, mind and spirit?

[ ] Who or what do I need to be aware of and why?

[ ] When did I feel good today? When did I not?

[ ] How can I replenish and recharge my energy?

[ ] What is one positive step I will take to protect my energy?

[ ] What are 5 positives about me?

_____

_____

_____

_____

_____

_____

_____

_____

_____

_____

_____

_____

_____

_____

_____

_____

_____

_____

_____

_____

_____

_____

_____

Journal Entries

Date: _____

Right Now I Feel: ___ Introvert ___ Extrovert ___ Ambivert

Rate Your Energy Level: _____

Prompts:

[ ] Where did I lose energy today in my body, mind and spirit?

[ ] Who or what do I need to be aware of and why?

[ ] When did I feel good today? When did I not?

[ ] How can I replenish and recharge my energy?

[ ] What is one positive step I will take to protect my energy?

[ ] What are 5 positives about me?

_____

_____

_____

_____

_____

_____

_____

_____

_____

_____

_____

_____

_____

_____

_____

_____

_____

_____

_____

_____

_____

_____

_____

_____

Journal Entries

Date: _____

Right Now I Feel: ___ Introvert ___ Extrovert ___ Ambivert

Rate Your Energy Level: _____

Prompts:

[ ] Where did I lose energy today in my body, mind and spirit?

[ ] Who or what do I need to be aware of and why?

[ ] When did I feel good today? When did I not?

[ ] How can I replenish and recharge my energy?

[ ] What is one positive step I will take to protect my energy?

[ ] What are 5 positives about me?

_____

_____

_____

_____

_____

_____

_____

_____

_____

_____

_____

_____

_____

_____

_____

_____

_____

_____

_____

_____

_____

_____

Journal Entries

Date: _____

Right Now I Feel: ___ Introvert __ Extrovert __ Ambivert

Rate Your Energy Level: _____

Prompts:

[ ] Where did I lose energy today in my body, mind and spirit?

[ ] Who or what do I need to be aware of and why?

[ ] When did I feel good today? When did I not?

[ ] How can I replenish and recharge my energy?

[ ] What is one positive step I will take to protect my energy?

[ ] What are 5 positives about me?

_____
_____
_____
_____
_____
_____
_____
_____
_____
_____
_____
_____
_____
_____
_____
_____
_____
_____
_____
_____
_____
_____

Journal Entries

Date: _____

Right Now I Feel: ___ Introvert ___ Extrovert ___ Ambivert

Rate Your Energy Level: _____

Prompts:

[ ] Where did I lose energy today in my body, mind and spirit?

[ ] Who or what do I need to be aware of and why?

[ ] When did I feel good today? When did I not?

[ ] How can I replenish and recharge my energy?

[ ] What is one positive step I will take to protect my energy?

[ ] What are 5 positives about me?

_____

_____

_____

_____

_____

_____

_____

_____

_____

_____

_____

_____

_____

_____

_____

_____

_____

_____

_____

_____

_____

_____

_____

Journal Entries

Date: _____

Right Now I Feel: ___ Introvert ___ Extrovert ___ Ambivert

Rate Your Energy Level: _____

Prompts:

[ ] Where did I lose energy today in my body, mind and spirit?

[ ] Who or what do I need to be aware of and why?

[ ] When did I feel good today? When did I not?

[ ] How can I replenish and recharge my energy?

[ ] What is one positive step I will take to protect my energy?

[ ] What are 5 positives about me?

_____
_____
_____
_____
_____
_____
_____
_____
_____
_____
_____
_____
_____
_____
_____
_____
_____
_____
_____
_____
_____
_____
_____

Journal Entries

Date: _____

Right Now I Feel: ___ Introvert ___ Extrovert ___ Ambivert

Rate Your Energy Level: _____

Prompts:

[ ] Where did I lose energy today in my body, mind and spirit?

[ ] Who or what do I need to be aware of and why?

[ ] When did I feel good today? When did I not?

[ ] How can I replenish and recharge my energy?

[ ] What is one positive step I will take to protect my energy?

[ ] What are 5 positives about me?

_____
_____
_____
_____
_____
_____
_____
_____
_____
_____
_____
_____
_____
_____
_____
_____
_____
_____
_____
_____
_____
_____
_____
_____
_____

Journal Entries

Date: _____

Right Now I Feel: ___ Introvert __ Extrovert __ Ambivert

Rate Your Energy Level: _____

Prompts:

[ ] Where did I lose energy today in my body, mind and spirit?

[ ] Who or what do I need to be aware of and why?

[ ] When did I feel good today? When did I not?

[ ] How can I replenish and recharge my energy?

[ ] What is one positive step I will take to protect my energy?

[ ] What are 5 positives about me?

_____

_____

_____

_____

_____

_____

_____

_____

_____

_____

_____

_____

_____

_____

_____

_____

_____

_____

_____

_____

_____

_____

Journal Entries

Date: _____

Right Now I Feel: ___ Introvert ___ Extrovert ___ Ambivert

Rate Your Energy Level: _____

Prompts:

[ ] Where did I lose energy today in my body, mind and spirit?

[ ] Who or what do I need to be aware of and why?

[ ] When did I feel good today? When did I not?

[ ] How can I replenish and recharge my energy?

[ ] What is one positive step I will take to protect my energy?

[ ] What are 5 positives about me?

_____
_____
_____
_____
_____
_____
_____
_____
_____
_____
_____
_____
_____
_____
_____
_____
_____
_____
_____
_____
_____
_____
_____
_____

Journal Entries

Date: _____

Right Now I Feel: ___ Introvert __ Extrovert __ Ambivert

Rate Your Energy Level: _____

Prompts:

[ ] Where did I lose energy today in my body, mind and spirit?

[ ] Who or what do I need to be aware of and why?

[ ] When did I feel good today? When did I not?

[ ] How can I replenish and recharge my energy?

[ ] What is one positive step I will take to protect my energy?

[ ] What are 5 positives about me?

_____

_____

_____

_____

_____

_____

_____

_____

_____

_____

_____

_____

_____

_____

_____

_____

_____

_____

_____

_____

_____

_____

_____

Journal Entries

Date: _____

Right Now I Feel: ___ Introvert __ Extrovert __ Ambivert

Rate Your Energy Level: _____

Prompts:

[ ] Where did I lose energy today in my body, mind and spirit?

[ ] Who or what do I need to be aware of and why?

[ ] When did I feel good today? When did I not?

[ ] How can I replenish and recharge my energy?

[ ] What is one positive step I will take to protect my energy?

[ ] What are 5 positives about me?

_____

_____

_____

_____

_____

_____

_____

_____

_____

_____

_____

_____

_____

_____

_____

_____

_____

_____

_____

_____

_____

_____

_____

Journal Entries

Date: _____

Right Now I Feel: ___ Introvert __ Extrovert __ Ambivert

Rate Your Energy Level: _____

Prompts:

[ ] Where did I lose energy today in my body, mind and spirit?

[ ] Who or what do I need to be aware of and why?

[ ] When did I feel good today? When did I not?

[ ] How can I replenish and recharge my energy?

[ ] What is one positive step I will take to protect my energy?

[ ] What are 5 positives about me?

_____

_____

_____

_____

_____

_____

_____

_____

_____

_____

_____

_____

_____

_____

_____

_____

_____

_____

_____

_____

_____

Journal Entries

Date: _____

Right Now I Feel: ___ Introvert __ Extrovert __ Ambivert

Rate Your Energy Level: _____

Prompts:

[ ] Where did I lose energy today in my body, mind and spirit?

[ ] Who or what do I need to be aware of and why?

[ ] When did I feel good today? When did I not?

[ ] How can I replenish and recharge my energy?

[ ] What is one positive step I will take to protect my energy?

[ ] What are 5 positives about me?

_____

_____

_____

_____

_____

_____

_____

_____

_____

_____

_____

_____

_____

_____

_____

_____

_____

_____

_____

_____

_____

Journal Entries

Date: _____

Right Now I Feel: ___ Introvert __ Extrovert __ Ambivert

Rate Your Energy Level: _____

Prompts:

[ ] Where did I lose energy today in my body, mind and spirit?

[ ] Who or what do I need to be aware of and why?

[ ] When did I feel good today? When did I not?

[ ] How can I replenish and recharge my energy?

[ ] What is one positive step I will take to protect my energy?

[ ] What are 5 positives about me?

_____

_____

_____

_____

_____

_____

_____

_____

_____

_____

_____

_____

_____

_____

_____

_____

_____

_____

_____

_____

Journal Entries

Date: _____

Right Now I Feel: ____ Introvert __ Extrovert __ Ambivert

Rate Your Energy Level: _____

Prompts:

[ ] Where did I lose energy today in my body, mind and spirit?

[ ] Who or what do I need to be aware of and why?

[ ] When did I feel good today? When did I not?

[ ] How can I replenish and recharge my energy?

[ ] What is one positive step I will take to protect my energy?

[ ] What are 5 positives about me?

_____
_____
_____
_____
_____
_____
_____
_____
_____
_____
_____
_____
_____
_____
_____
_____
_____
_____
_____
_____
_____
_____
_____

Journal Entries

Date: _____

Right Now I Feel: ___ Introvert ___ Extrovert ___ Ambivert

Rate Your Energy Level: _____

Prompts:

[ ] Where did I lose energy today in my body, mind and spirit?

[ ] Who or what do I need to be aware of and why?

[ ] When did I feel good today? When did I not?

[ ] How can I replenish and recharge my energy?

[ ] What is one positive step I will take to protect my energy?

[ ] What are 5 positives about me?

_____

_____

_____

_____

_____

_____

_____

_____

_____

_____

_____

_____

_____

_____

_____

_____

_____

_____

_____

_____

_____

_____

_____

Journal Entries

Date: _____

Right Now I Feel: ___ Introvert __ Extrovert __ Ambivert

Rate Your Energy Level: _____

Prompts:

[ ] Where did I lose energy today in my body, mind and spirit?

[ ] Who or what do I need to be aware of and why?

[ ] When did I feel good today? When did I not?

[ ] How can I replenish and recharge my energy?

[ ] What is one positive step I will take to protect my energy?

[ ] What are 5 positives about me?

_____

_____

_____

_____

_____

_____

_____

_____

_____

_____

_____

_____

_____

_____

_____

_____

_____

_____

_____

_____

_____

_____

Journal Entries

Date: _____

Right Now I Feel: ___ Introvert __ Extrovert __ Ambivert

Rate Your Energy Level: _____

Prompts:

[ ] Where did I lose energy today in my body, mind and spirit?

[ ] Who or what do I need to be aware of and why?

[ ] When did I feel good today? When did I not?

[ ] How can I replenish and recharge my energy?

[ ] What is one positive step I will take to protect my energy?

[ ] What are 5 positives about me?

_____

_____

_____

_____

_____

_____

_____

_____

_____

_____

_____

_____

_____

_____

_____

_____

_____

_____

_____

_____

_____

Journal Entries

Date: _____

Right Now I Feel: ___ Introvert __ Extrovert __ Ambivert

Rate Your Energy Level: _____

Prompts:

[ ] Where did I lose energy today in my body, mind and spirit?

[ ] Who or what do I need to be aware of and why?

[ ] When did I feel good today? When did I not?

[ ] How can I replenish and recharge my energy?

[ ] What is one positive step I will take to protect my energy?

[ ] What are 5 positives about me?

_____
_____
_____
_____
_____
_____
_____
_____
_____
_____
_____
_____
_____
_____
_____
_____
_____
_____
_____
_____
_____
_____
_____

Journal Entries

Date: _____

Right Now I Feel: ___ Introvert __ Extrovert __ Ambivert

Rate Your Energy Level: _____

Prompts:

[ ] Where did I lose energy today in my body, mind and spirit?

[ ] Who or what do I need to be aware of and why?

[ ] When did I feel good today? When did I not?

[ ] How can I replenish and recharge my energy?

[ ] What is one positive step I will take to protect my energy?

[ ] What are 5 positives about me?

_____
_____
_____
_____
_____
_____
_____
_____
_____
_____
_____
_____
_____
_____
_____
_____
_____
_____
_____
_____
_____
_____
_____

Journal Entries

Date: _____

Right Now I Feel: ____ Introvert ___ Extrovert ___ Ambivert

Rate Your Energy Level: _____

Prompts:

[ ] Where did I lose energy today in my body, mind and spirit?

[ ] Who or what do I need to be aware of and why?

[ ] When did I feel good today? When did I not?

[ ] How can I replenish and recharge my energy?

[ ] What is one positive step I will take to protect my energy?

[ ] What are 5 positives about me?

_____

_____

_____

_____

_____

_____

_____

_____

_____

_____

_____

_____

_____

_____

_____

_____

_____

_____

_____

_____

_____

_____

Journal Entries

Date: _____

Right Now I Feel: ___ Introvert __ Extrovert __ Ambivert

Rate Your Energy Level: _____

Prompts:

[ ] Where did I lose energy today in my body, mind and spirit?

[ ] Who or what do I need to be aware of and why?

[ ] When did I feel good today? When did I not?

[ ] How can I replenish and recharge my energy?

[ ] What is one positive step I will take to protect my energy?

[ ] What are 5 positives about me?

_____

_____

_____

_____

_____

_____

_____

_____

_____

_____

_____

_____

_____

_____

_____

_____

_____

_____

_____

_____

_____

_____

_____

Journal Entries

Date: _____

Right Now I Feel: ___ Introvert __ Extrovert __ Ambivert

Rate Your Energy Level: _____

Prompts:

[ ] Where did I lose energy today in my body, mind and spirit?

[ ] Who or what do I need to be aware of and why?

[ ] When did I feel good today? When did I not?

[ ] How can I replenish and recharge my energy?

[ ] What is one positive step I will take to protect my energy?

[ ] What are 5 positives about me?

_____
_____
_____
_____
_____
_____
_____
_____
_____
_____
_____
_____
_____
_____
_____
_____
_____
_____
_____
_____
_____
_____

Journal Entries

Date: _____

Right Now I Feel: ___ Introvert __ Extrovert __ Ambivert

Rate Your Energy Level: _____

Prompts:

[ ] Where did I lose energy today in my body, mind and spirit?

[ ] Who or what do I need to be aware of and why?

[ ] When did I feel good today? When did I not?

[ ] How can I replenish and recharge my energy?

[ ] What is one positive step I will take to protect my energy?

[ ] What are 5 positives about me?

_____

_____

_____

_____

_____

_____

_____

_____

_____

_____

_____

_____

_____

_____

_____

_____

_____

_____

_____

_____

_____

_____

_____

Journal Entries

Date: _____

Right Now I Feel: ___ Introvert __ Extrovert __ Ambivert

Rate Your Energy Level: _____

Prompts:

[ ] Where did I lose energy today in my body, mind and spirit?

[ ] Who or what do I need to be aware of and why?

[ ] When did I feel good today? When did I not?

[ ] How can I replenish and recharge my energy?

[ ] What is one positive step I will take to protect my energy?

[ ] What are 5 positives about me?

_____
_____
_____
_____
_____
_____
_____
_____
_____
_____
_____
_____
_____
_____
_____
_____
_____
_____
_____
_____
_____
_____

Journal Entries

Date: _____

Right Now I Feel: ___ Introvert __ Extrovert __ Ambivert

Rate Your Energy Level: _____

Prompts:

[ ] Where did I lose energy today in my body, mind and spirit?

[ ] Who or what do I need to be aware of and why?

[ ] When did I feel good today? When did I not?

[ ] How can I replenish and recharge my energy?

[ ] What is one positive step I will take to protect my energy?

[ ] What are 5 positives about me?

_____

_____

_____

_____

_____

_____

_____

_____

_____

_____

_____

_____

_____

_____

_____

_____

_____

_____

_____

_____

_____

_____

Journal Entries

Date: _____

Right Now I Feel: ___ Introvert __ Extrovert __ Ambivert

Rate Your Energy Level: _____

Prompts:

[ ] Where did I lose energy today in my body, mind and spirit?

[ ] Who or what do I need to be aware of and why?

[ ] When did I feel good today? When did I not?

[ ] How can I replenish and recharge my energy?

[ ] What is one positive step I will take to protect my energy?

[ ] What are 5 positives about me?

_____

_____

_____

_____

_____

_____

_____

_____

_____

_____

_____

_____

_____

_____

_____

_____

_____

_____

_____

_____

_____

_____

Journal Entries

Date: _____

Right Now I Feel: ___ Introvert ___ Extrovert ___ Ambivert

Rate Your Energy Level: _____

Prompts:

[ ] Where did I lose energy today in my body, mind and spirit?

[ ] Who or what do I need to be aware of and why?

[ ] When did I feel good today? When did I not?

[ ] How can I replenish and recharge my energy?

[ ] What is one positive step I will take to protect my energy?

[ ] What are 5 positives about me?

_____
_____
_____
_____
_____
_____
_____
_____
_____
_____
_____
_____
_____
_____
_____
_____
_____
_____
_____
_____
_____
_____
_____

Journal Entries

Date: _____

Right Now I Feel: ___ Introvert __ Extrovert __ Ambivert

Rate Your Energy Level: _____

Prompts:

[ ] Where did I lose energy today in my body, mind and spirit?

[ ] Who or what do I need to be aware of and why?

[ ] When did I feel good today? When did I not?

[ ] How can I replenish and recharge my energy?

[ ] What is one positive step I will take to protect my energy?

[ ] What are 5 positives about me?

_____

_____

_____

_____

_____

_____

_____

_____

_____

_____

_____

_____

_____

_____

_____

_____

_____

_____

_____

_____

_____

_____

Journal Entries

Date: _____

Right Now I Feel: ___ Introvert ___ Extrovert ___ Ambivert

Rate Your Energy Level: _____

Prompts:

[ ] Where did I lose energy today in my body, mind and spirit?

[ ] Who or what do I need to be aware of and why?

[ ] When did I feel good today? When did I not?

[ ] How can I replenish and recharge my energy?

[ ] What is one positive step I will take to protect my energy?

[ ] What are 5 positives about me?

_____
_____
_____
_____
_____
_____
_____
_____
_____
_____
_____
_____
_____
_____
_____
_____
_____
_____
_____
_____
_____
_____
_____

Journal Entries

Date: _____

Right Now I Feel: ___ Introvert ___ Extrovert ___ Ambivert

Rate Your Energy Level: _____

Prompts:

[ ] Where did I lose energy today in my body, mind and spirit?

[ ] Who or what do I need to be aware of and why?

[ ] When did I feel good today? When did I not?

[ ] How can I replenish and recharge my energy?

[ ] What is one positive step I will take to protect my energy?

[ ] What are 5 positives about me?

_____
_____
_____
_____
_____
_____
_____
_____
_____
_____
_____
_____
_____
_____
_____
_____
_____
_____
_____
_____
_____
_____
_____
_____

Journal Entries

Date: _____

Right Now I Feel: ____ Introvert __ Extrovert __ Ambivert

Rate Your Energy Level: _____

Prompts:

[ ] Where did I lose energy today in my body, mind and spirit?

[ ] Who or what do I need to be aware of and why?

[ ] When did I feel good today? When did I not?

[ ] How can I replenish and recharge my energy?

[ ] What is one positive step I will take to protect my energy?

[ ] What are 5 positives about me?

_____
_____
_____
_____
_____
_____
_____
_____
_____
_____
_____
_____
_____
_____
_____
_____
_____
_____
_____
_____
_____
_____
_____
_____
_____

Journal Entries

Date: _____

Right Now I Feel: ___ Introvert __ Extrovert __ Ambivert

Rate Your Energy Level: _____

Prompts:

[ ] Where did I lose energy today in my body, mind and spirit?

[ ] Who or what do I need to be aware of and why?

[ ] When did I feel good today? When did I not?

[ ] How can I replenish and recharge my energy?

[ ] What is one positive step I will take to protect my energy?

[ ] What are 5 positives about me?

_____
_____
_____
_____
_____
_____
_____
_____
_____
_____
_____
_____
_____
_____
_____
_____
_____
_____
_____
_____
_____
_____
_____

Journal Entries

Date: _____

Right Now I Feel: ___ Introvert __ Extrovert __ Ambivert

Rate Your Energy Level: _____

Prompts:

[ ] Where did I lose energy today in my body, mind and spirit?

[ ] Who or what do I need to be aware of and why?

[ ] When did I feel good today? When did I not?

[ ] How can I replenish and recharge my energy?

[ ] What is one positive step I will take to protect my energy?

[ ] What are 5 positives about me?

_____
_____
_____
_____
_____
_____
_____
_____
_____
_____
_____
_____
_____
_____
_____
_____
_____
_____
_____
_____
_____
_____
_____

Journal Entries

Date: _____

Right Now I Feel: ___ Introvert __ Extrovert __ Ambivert

Rate Your Energy Level: _____

Prompts:

[ ] Where did I lose energy today in my body, mind and spirit?

[ ] Who or what do I need to be aware of and why?

[ ] When did I feel good today? When did I not?

[ ] How can I replenish and recharge my energy?

[ ] What is one positive step I will take to protect my energy?

[ ] What are 5 positives about me?

_____

_____

_____

_____

_____

_____

_____

_____

_____

_____

_____

_____

_____

_____

_____

_____

_____

_____

_____

_____

_____

_____

_____

Journal Entries

Date: _____

Right Now I Feel: ___ Introvert __ Extrovert __ Ambivert

Rate Your Energy Level: _____

Prompts:

[ ] Where did I lose energy today in my body, mind and spirit?

[ ] Who or what do I need to be aware of and why?

[ ] When did I feel good today? When did I not?

[ ] How can I replenish and recharge my energy?

[ ] What is one positive step I will take to protect my energy?

[ ] What are 5 positives about me?

_____
_____
_____
_____
_____
_____
_____
_____
_____
_____
_____
_____
_____
_____
_____
_____
_____
_____
_____
_____
_____
_____
_____
_____
_____

Journal Entries

Date: _____

Right Now I Feel: ___ Introvert ___ Extrovert ___ Ambivert

Rate Your Energy Level: _____

Prompts:

[ ] Where did I lose energy today in my body, mind and spirit?

[ ] Who or what do I need to be aware of and why?

[ ] When did I feel good today? When did I not?

[ ] How can I replenish and recharge my energy?

[ ] What is one positive step I will take to protect my energy?

[ ] What are 5 positives about me?

_____

_____

_____

_____

_____

_____

_____

_____

_____

_____

_____

_____

_____

_____

_____

_____

_____

_____

_____

_____

_____

_____

Journal Entries

Date: _____

Right Now I Feel: ___ Introvert ___ Extrovert ___ Ambivert

Rate Your Energy Level: _____

Prompts:

[ ] Where did I lose energy today in my body, mind and spirit?

[ ] Who or what do I need to be aware of and why?

[ ] When did I feel good today? When did I not?

[ ] How can I replenish and recharge my energy?

[ ] What is one positive step I will take to protect my energy?

[ ] What are 5 positives about me?

_____
_____
_____
_____
_____
_____
_____
_____
_____
_____
_____
_____
_____
_____
_____
_____
_____
_____
_____
_____
_____
_____
_____

Journal Entries

Date: _____

Right Now I Feel: ___ Introvert __ Extrovert __ Ambivert

Rate Your Energy Level: _____

Prompts:

[ ] Where did I lose energy today in my body, mind and spirit?

[ ] Who or what do I need to be aware of and why?

[ ] When did I feel good today? When did I not?

[ ] How can I replenish and recharge my energy?

[ ] What is one positive step I will take to protect my energy?

[ ] What are 5 positives about me?

_____

_____

_____

_____

_____

_____

_____

_____

_____

_____

_____

_____

_____

_____

_____

_____

_____

_____

_____

_____

_____

_____

_____

Journal Entries

Date: _____

Right Now I Feel: ___ Introvert ___ Extrovert ___ Ambivert

Rate Your Energy Level: _____

Prompts:

[ ] Where did I lose energy today in my body, mind and spirit?

[ ] Who or what do I need to be aware of and why?

[ ] When did I feel good today? When did I not?

[ ] How can I replenish and recharge my energy?

[ ] What is one positive step I will take to protect my energy?

[ ] What are 5 positives about me?

_____

_____

_____

_____

_____

_____

_____

_____

_____

_____

_____

_____

_____

_____

_____

_____

_____

_____

_____

_____

_____

_____

_____

Journal Entries

Date: _____

Right Now I Feel: ___ Introvert __ Extrovert __ Ambivert

Rate Your Energy Level: _____

Prompts:

[ ] Where did I lose energy today in my body, mind and spirit?

[ ] Who or what do I need to be aware of and why?

[ ] When did I feel good today? When did I not?

[ ] How can I replenish and recharge my energy?

[ ] What is one positive step I will take to protect my energy?

[ ] What are 5 positives about me?

_____

_____

_____

_____

_____

_____

_____

_____

_____

_____

_____

_____

_____

_____

_____

_____

_____

_____

_____

_____

_____

_____

_____

_____

Journal Entries

Date: _____

Right Now I Feel: ___ Introvert __ Extrovert __ Ambivert

Rate Your Energy Level: _____

Prompts:

[ ] Where did I lose energy today in my body, mind and spirit?

[ ] Who or what do I need to be aware of and why?

[ ] When did I feel good today? When did I not?

[ ] How can I replenish and recharge my energy?

[ ] What is one positive step I will take to protect my energy?

[ ] What are 5 positives about me?

_____

_____

_____

_____

_____

_____

_____

_____

_____

_____

_____

_____

_____

_____

_____

_____

_____

_____

_____

_____

_____

_____

_____

Journal Entries

Date: _____

Right Now I Feel: ___ Introvert __ Extrovert __ Ambivert

Rate Your Energy Level: _____

Prompts:

[ ] Where did I lose energy today in my body, mind and spirit?

[ ] Who or what do I need to be aware of and why?

[ ] When did I feel good today? When did I not?

[ ] How can I replenish and recharge my energy?

[ ] What is one positive step I will take to protect my energy?

[ ] What are 5 positives about me?

_____
_____
_____
_____
_____
_____
_____
_____
_____
_____
_____
_____
_____
_____
_____
_____
_____
_____
_____
_____
_____
_____
_____
_____

Journal Entries

Date: _____

Right Now I Feel: ___ Introvert __ Extrovert __ Ambivert

Rate Your Energy Level: _____

Prompts:

[ ] Where did I lose energy today in my body, mind and spirit?

[ ] Who or what do I need to be aware of and why?

[ ] When did I feel good today? When did I not?

[ ] How can I replenish and recharge my energy?

[ ] What is one positive step I will take to protect my energy?

[ ] What are 5 positives about me?

_____

_____

_____

_____

_____

_____

_____

_____

_____

_____

_____

_____

_____

_____

_____

_____

_____

_____

_____

_____

_____

_____

Journal Entries

Date: _____

Right Now I Feel: ___ Introvert ___ Extrovert ___ Ambivert

Rate Your Energy Level: _____

Prompts:

[ ] Where did I lose energy today in my body, mind and spirit?

[ ] Who or what do I need to be aware of and why?

[ ] When did I feel good today? When did I not?

[ ] How can I replenish and recharge my energy?

[ ] What is one positive step I will take to protect my energy?

[ ] What are 5 positives about me?

_____

_____

_____

_____

_____

_____

_____

_____

_____

_____

_____

_____

_____

_____

_____

_____

_____

_____

_____

_____

_____

_____

_____

Journal Entries

Date: _____

Right Now I Feel: ___ Introvert __ Extrovert __ Ambivert

Rate Your Energy Level: _____

Prompts:

[ ] Where did I lose energy today in my body, mind and spirit?

[ ] Who or what do I need to be aware of and why?

[ ] When did I feel good today? When did I not?

[ ] How can I replenish and recharge my energy?

[ ] What is one positive step I will take to protect my energy?

[ ] What are 5 positives about me?

_____

_____

_____

_____

_____

_____

_____

_____

_____

_____

_____

_____

_____

_____

_____

_____

_____

_____

_____

_____

_____

_____

_____

Journal Entries

Date: _____

Right Now I Feel: ___ Introvert __ Extrovert __ Ambivert

Rate Your Energy Level: _____

Prompts:

[ ] Where did I lose energy today in my body, mind and spirit?

[ ] Who or what do I need to be aware of and why?

[ ] When did I feel good today? When did I not?

[ ] How can I replenish and recharge my energy?

[ ] What is one positive step I will take to protect my energy?

[ ] What are 5 positives about me?

_____

_____

_____

_____

_____

_____

_____

_____

_____

_____

_____

_____

_____

_____

_____

_____

_____

_____

_____

_____

_____

Journal Entries

Date: _____

Right Now I Feel: ___ Introvert __ Extrovert __ Ambivert

Rate Your Energy Level: _____

Prompts:

[ ] Where did I lose energy today in my body, mind and spirit?

[ ] Who or what do I need to be aware of and why?

[ ] When did I feel good today? When did I not?

[ ] How can I replenish and recharge my energy?

[ ] What is one positive step I will take to protect my energy?

[ ] What are 5 positives about me?

_____
_____
_____
_____
_____
_____
_____
_____
_____
_____
_____
_____
_____
_____
_____
_____
_____
_____
_____
_____
_____
_____
_____

Journal Entries

Date: _____

Right Now I Feel: ___ Introvert ___ Extrovert ___ Ambivert

Rate Your Energy Level: _____

Prompts:

[ ] Where did I lose energy today in my body, mind and spirit?

[ ] Who or what do I need to be aware of and why?

[ ] When did I feel good today? When did I not?

[ ] How can I replenish and recharge my energy?

[ ] What is one positive step I will take to protect my energy?

[ ] What are 5 positives about me?

_____

_____

_____

_____

_____

_____

_____

_____

_____

_____

_____

_____

_____

_____

_____

_____

_____

_____

_____

_____

_____

_____

_____

Journal Entries

Date: _____

Right Now I Feel: ___ Introvert ___ Extrovert ___ Ambivert

Rate Your Energy Level: _____

Prompts:

[ ] Where did I lose energy today in my body, mind and spirit?

[ ] Who or what do I need to be aware of and why?

[ ] When did I feel good today? When did I not?

[ ] How can I replenish and recharge my energy?

[ ] What is one positive step I will take to protect my energy?

[ ] What are 5 positives about me?

_____
_____
_____
_____
_____
_____
_____
_____
_____
_____
_____
_____
_____
_____
_____
_____
_____
_____
_____
_____
_____
_____
_____
_____

Journal Entries

Date: _____

Right Now I Feel: ___ Introvert __ Extrovert __ Ambivert

Rate Your Energy Level: _____

Prompts:

[ ] Where did I lose energy today in my body, mind and spirit?

[ ] Who or what do I need to be aware of and why?

[ ] When did I feel good today? When did I not?

[ ] How can I replenish and recharge my energy?

[ ] What is one positive step I will take to protect my energy?

[ ] What are 5 positives about me?

_____

_____

_____

_____

_____

_____

_____

_____

_____

_____

_____

_____

_____

_____

_____

_____

_____

_____

_____

_____

_____

_____

_____

_____

Now You Have Finished

If you have filled in all of the spaces in this journal, you have completed ten to eleven weeks of energy management practices. Congratulations!

What is next?

You can continue your self-analysis with these exercises and/or contact me for a free consult call to see if our energies would be a good match to work together. I have created a unique counseling and coaching program to work with professionals, like you, who get drained from your helping efforts. Together, we formulate a specific plan to rejuvenate and restore your energy. These services are offered in person and by phone.

Find your center when life feels overwhelming and increase your coping skills with my FREE gift to you, a 10 page E-book; 8 Simple Things That Release Chaos from Your Life Now! Sign up for it and my monthly newsletter at http://www.lisahutchison.net

I would love if you would revisit this journal on Amazon and leave a review. Feel free to contact me at lisadhutch@verizon.net and tell me your feedback and progress.

Many Blessings,

Lisa

Lisa Hutchison LMHC- Licensed Psychotherapist & Writing Coach

Connect with me- Let's stay in touch!

My blog: https://connectingempathichelpersandartiststospirit.wordpress.com/

Twitter: https://twitter.com/Connectsp_lisah

Facebook:
https://www.facebook.com/Connectingempathichelpersandartiststospirit/

LinkedIn: https://www.linkedin.com/in/lisahutchison1/

Pinterest: https://www.pinterest.com/lisadhutch/

Made in the USA
Columbia, SC
10 April 2023

15178094R00098